C

BBC CHILDREN'S BOOKS

Pingu wants to bring home a fish.

Now Pingu and Robby are hungry.

Robby thinks his friend is very clever.

He has a good idea.

Pingu gets dizzy.

The fish is stuck on the washing line.

The two friends play tennis.

Robby pulls the fish off Pingu's head.

But it slips down.

He puts the fish on his head.

Pingu falls down.

Robby catches the fish on his nose.

He has brought a fish to play with.

Robby waits for Pingu to wake up.

PINGU
Plays Fish Tennis

Now Pingu has a new friend.

Robby gives Pingu a huge fish.

Pingu didn't mean to hurt Robby.

They chase each other.

Pingu knows how to tease Robby.

Robby the seal likes playing.

Now he knows who was pulling.

Pingu can hardly hold on to his rod.

But what is Robby the seal up to?

A fish already!

Fish love seaweed.

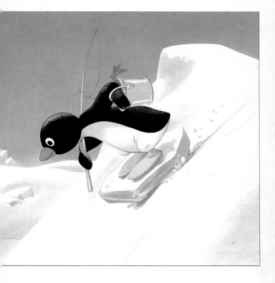

He slides down the hill on an ice block.